The EF Book

by Lynn Maslen Kertell
pictures by Sue Hendra and John R. Maslen

Scholastic Inc.
New York • Toronto • London • Auckland • Sydney • Mexico City • New Delhi • Hong Kong • Buenos Aires

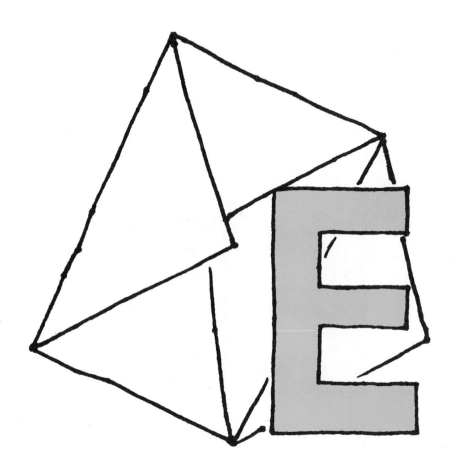

Envelope

egg

Elephant and elk are excited to

watch an eagle hatch from an egg.

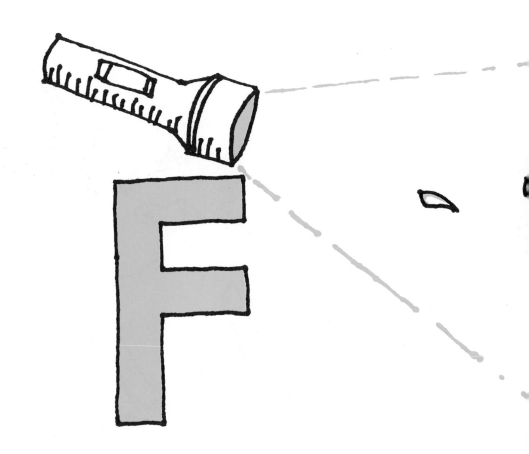

Flashlight

frog

Frog, fish, and fox

frolic in a fountain.

The fountain fills up when elk,

eagle, and elephant enter.

Look for these **e** and **f** words in this book.

eagle	fills
egg	fish
elephant	flashlight
elk	fountain
enter	fox
envelope	frog
excited	frolic

Look for these additional **e** and **f** words in the pictures: ears, eggshells, eyes, feathers, ferns, fins, fireflies, and flower.